blu rise

WISE PUBLICATIONS
London / New York / Paris / Sydney / Copenhagen / Berlin / Madrid / Tokyo

simon
antony

lee   duncan

all rise

**Words & Music by Mikkel SE, Hallgeir Rustan,
Tor Erik Hermansen & Simon Webbe**

low, leav - ing all my op - tions op - en the de - ci - sion of the ju - ry has not been spo - ken. Step in my

house, you find that your stuff has gone. But in re - al - i - ty to whom does the stuff be - long? I bring you

in - to court to preach my or - der_ and you know that you ov - er - stepped the bor - der. A - ha.

Cm   Gm⁷   Cm   E♭

One for the mo - ney and the free rides. It's two for the lie that you de - nied. All

rise, all rise. Three for the calls you've been mak - ing. It's

four all the times you've been fak - ing. All rise, all rise.

rise, all rise.
(I'm gon - na tell it to your face, I rest my case.)

Verse 2:
You're on the stand
With your back against the wall
Nowhere to run
And nobody you can call
I just can't wait
Now the case is open wide
You'll try to pray
But the jury will decide.

Baby I swear I'll tell the truth *etc.*

too close

Words & Music by Keir Gist, Darren Lighty, Robert Huggar, Raphael Brown, Robert Ford, Denzil Miller, James Moore, Kurt Walker & Lawrence Smith

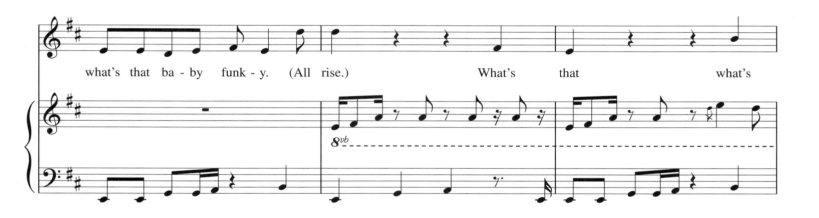

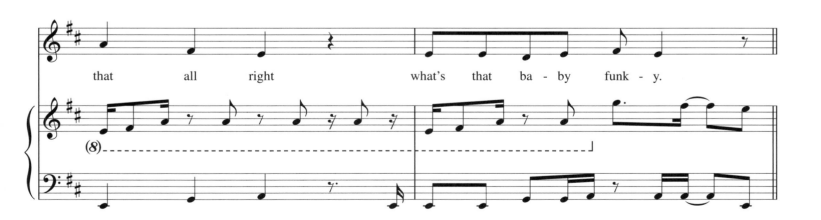

girl I know you felt it, be-fore you know_ I can't help_ it.___ You know what I want_

1. ___ to do.___ Oh, **2.** ___ to do.___ Ba-by, when we're grind-ing

I get so ex-ci - ted. Oh,_ how I like_ it. I try but I__ can't fight_ it.

Oh, you're danc-ing real close,_ plus it's real,_ real slow._ You're mak-ing it hard_

12

Verse 2:
Baby, us dancing so close
Ain't a good idea
'Cause I might want you now and here
The way that you shake it on me
Makes me want you so bad sexually.

Step back you're dancing kind of close   *etc.*

this temptation

Words & Music by Eliot Kennedy, Steve Richards, Simon Webbe,
Antony Costa, Duncan Inglis & Lee Ryan

me. But now the mo - ment's come,_ I've nev - er been good at this temp - ta - tion.
1. From the

first time_ it felt so right,_ I knew that
(Verse 2 see block lyric)

right here_ is where I be - longed._____ With that

black dress, I have to con - fess_ my in -

I've nev-er been good at this temp-ta-tion.

(This temp-ta-tion.)

I know that we've both been here be-fore. That's why I real-ly want to be sure. But now the mo-ment's here I've nev-er been too good at this temp-ta-tion.

Verse 2:
Every night you've been on my mind
Could you be the one I've been waiting for?
'Cause your sweetest kiss, oh, I just can't resist
That's the kind of thing you've got me begging for more.

(Hold on) This ain't the right time   *etc.*

if you come back

Words & Music by Ray Ruffin, Nicole Formescu, Ian Hope & Lee Brennan

Come on! Yeah,___ can you feel me? Ba - by can you feel me?_

___ I got some - thin' to say, check it out.

1. For all___ this time___ I've been lov - in' you_
(Verse 2 see block lyric)

Verse 2:
I watched you go
Taking my heart with you
Oh, yes you did
Every time I try to reach you on the phone
Baby, you're never there
Girl, you're never home.

So if I did something wrong *etc.*

fly by

Words & Music by Mikkel SE, Hallgeir Rustan,
Tor Erik Hermansen & Simon Webbe

1. All dressed up you're good to go,_ check-in' your style from head to toe._ Hooked up and na-tur-al,_
(Verse 2 see block lyric)

you're feel-ing beau-ti-ful.__ Nine times out of ten you know,_ late night club like a vi-de-o.__ With the

hot stuff, top stuff, yo we got stuff. Oh._____ What a night (night)_ so__

far, (far)__ pull-ing up curb-side__ in your car.__ (Your__ car)_ What a

Verse 2:
Girl it's time to let you know
I'm down if you wanna go
We can take it nice and slow
We got until tomorrow
U.K. style U.K. flow
We got you hot like whoah
With the hot stuff - top - yo, we got stuff.

What a night so far *etc.*

long time

Words & Music by Ian Hope, Ray Ruffin, Antony Costa & Simon Webbe

the on-ly one I real-ly want___ and there's one___ thing you've got-ta know.___ It's gon-na be a

long,_____ long,___ long time_____ till I can be___

___ with you___ a-gain___ and see___ your smile. It's gon-na be a

long,_____ long,___ long time_____ till I

Verse 2:
Lookin' outside and I feel so uninspired
And it rains all through this lonely night, oh yeah
I'm losing my mind and my soul is feelin' 'tired
'Cause girl you are my guiding light, oh yeah.

It's gonna be a long, long, long time   *etc.*

make it happen

**Words & Music by Jan Kask, Peter Mansson,
Wayne Hector & Ali Tennant**

that I___ won't do___ you wrong.___ this love___ I feel___ is far___ too strong.__ 'Cause now___ I've wait - ed far_ too long,___ you can't__ just lay___ me on.___ Don't_ just talk_ ___ make_ it hap - pen. (Don't make me wait for you, do what you came to do.)

Keep me up, don't stop.____ Make_ it hap - pen. (It's got the best of me,

1.
this cu - ri - o - si - ty.) Don't_ just talk___ this cu - ri - o - si - ty.)

2.
It

kills me ev - 'ry time.____

Verse 2:
I waited for you to ring my bell
I want you to
So don't be late, quit playing games
Don't hesitate.

'Cause now I've waited far too long   *etc.*

bounce

Words & Music by Mikkel SE, Hallgeir Rustan,
Tor Erik Hermansen & Simon Webbe

You're the type of girl that I've been look-ing for. ___   1. I don't know

much, but one__ thing I know, you're mak-ing it hard to keep__ it down low. If you ev-er

(Verse 2 see block lyrics)

wan - na come__ to my show, V. I. P. back-stage, front__ row. Nev - er seen a

girl look - ing so fine, get a lit - tle vibe and it's__ a - bout time. Right be - side a

(High like that.)___ (echo)

___ Give, give me more, step on the floor. You're the type of girl that I've been look-ing for.

All the fel-la's in the house to-night,___ are you gon-na bounce, bounce with us to-night.___

Verse 2:
I don't know much but one thing I know
If you wanna stay I'm not gonna go
Tell me just a simple yes or a no
Not maybe, we'll see, don't know
Not about the things you think I will flash
Gotta realise you need you own cash
You don't have to worry 'bout my past
Just two girls, score card, first class
Rock you all night long
Till I lose control
I'll never let you go.

Give, give me more *etc.*

back to you

**Words & Music by Ian Hope, Ray Ruffin, Simon Webbe,
Antony Costa, Duncan Inglis & Lee Ryan**

51

cool guy, I don't want no has-sle. You be the queen_ I'll be the king of the cas-tle.

Come back, ba - by come back to me,____ you're all, girl you're all__ I need.__

_ Come back, ba - by come back to me._____ (Come on.)

Come back, ba - by come back to me,____ you're all, girl you're all__ I need.

Verse 2:
I wanna look into your eyes
And let the world just pass me by
When you're talking in your sleep
I know that I'm in too deep.

Everytime you call my name
You know I'm coming back to you   *etc.*

girl i'll never understand

Words & Music by Tim Woodcock & Gary Barlow

Verse 2:
Covered you in diamonds
Gave you somewhere in the sun
And at that moment
I had only just begun
Got you the designers
From every magazine
Maybe if I'd known then
All this pain inside would never be.

Girl you are a mystery
So glad that we're history
Guess we were never meant to be
But I'm doing fine but in my mind.

I could never believe *etc.*

back some day

Words & Music by Tim Woodcock & Mike Terry

Verse 2:
When I return I wanna see
If this beautiful baby is still loving me
With tears in her eyes
But a smile on her face
Patiently we'll embrace.

But it's not long now *etc.*

best in me

Words & Music by Bill Padley & Jem Godfrey

ev - er wan-na lose this feel - ing,_ I don't wan-na spend a mo-ment a - part._____ 'Cause

you bring_ out_ the best_ in_ me,_ like no - one else_ can do._____ That's why I'm by_

__ your side_ and that's why I love you.

you. (Ooh,___ ooh,___ ooh, ooh, ooh.)

(Vocal ad lib.)

Verse 2:
Every day that I'm here with you
I know that it feels right (so right)
I just gotta be near you
Every day and every night (every night)
And you know that we belong together
It just had to be you and me.

'Cause you bring out the best in me *etc.*

Exclusive distributors:
Music Sales Limited, 8/9 Frith Street, London W1D 3JB, England.
Music Sales Pty Limited, 120 Rothschild Avenue, Rosebery, NSW 2018, Australia.

Order No. AM974006
ISBN 0-7119-9401-3
This book © Copyright 2002 by Wise Publications.

Music arrangements by Derek Jones.
Music processed by Paul Ewers Music Design.
Images courtesy of Virgin Records Ltd.

Printed in the United Kingdom by Caligraving Limited, Thetford, Norfolk.

Your Guarantee of Quality:
As publishers, we strive to produce every book to the highest commercial standards.
While endeavouring to retain the original running order of the recorded album, the
book has been carefully designed to minimise awkward page turns and to make playing
from it a real pleasure.
Particular care has been given to specifying acid-free, neutral-sized paper made
from pulps which have not been elemental chlorine bleached. This pulp is from farmed
sustainable forests and was produced with special regard for the environment.
Throughout, the printing and binding have been planned to ensure a sturdy, attractive
publication which should give years of enjoyment.
If your copy fails to meet our high standards, please inform us and we will gladly replace it.

Music Sales' complete catalogue describes thousands of titles and is available in
full colour sections by subject, direct from Music Sales Limited.
Please state your areas of interest and send a cheque/postal order for £1.50 for postage to:
Music Sales Limited, Newmarket Road, Bury St. Edmunds, Suffolk IP33 3YB.

www.musicsales.com